THE LION'S CAVALCADE

THE LION'S CAVALCADE

by ALAN ALDRIDGE

Illustrated in collaboration with

HARRY WILLOCK

Poems by

TED WALKER

AURELIA ENTERPRISES LTD

PUBLISHED BY

JONATHAN CAPE THIRTY BEDFORD SQUARE LONDON

Also illustrated by Alan Aldridge

THE BUTTERFLY BALL AND THE GRASSHOPPER'S FEAST
with verses by William Plomer
THE SHIP'S CAT
with verses by Richard Adams
THE PEACOCK PARTY
with verses by George E. Ryder

First published 1980
Based on *The Lion's Masquerade and Elephant's Champêtre*
by A Lady (1808), a sequel to *The Peacock 'At Home'*

Illustrations and text © 1980 by Aurelia Enterprises Ltd
Jonathan Cape Ltd, 30 Bedford Square, London WC1

British Library Cataloguing in Publication Data

Aldridge, Alan
The lion's cavalcade.
I. Willock, Harry II. Walker, Ted
823'.9'IJ   PZ7.A371/
ISBN 0 224 01701 2

Printed in Italy by A. Mondadori Editore, Verona

THE WRATH OF ROYALTY

Leonis, King of the Jungle, was feeling low and jaded.
All the radiant colours of his inner rainbow faded
When Leonie de Lyonesse, his good and faithful wife,
Regaled him with the details of the Insects' social life.

"In Lepidoptera Province they have held an event
Too dazzling to describe — simply *everybody* went,"
Queen Leonie informed him. "Believe me, dear, I *know*,
For Daphne Mezereum, my maid, has told me so."

"We are disinclined to listen to reports of Gadfly jollity,
Of meretricious Moths and their desperate frivolity,"
The King exclaimed, "however much Mezereum enthused,
You may take it from us, my dear, that we are not amused.

"We are no romping cub forever bent on play and mirth:
We are dignified and middle-aged and ample in the girth.
A Sovereign spends a serious life — and Queens should spend their days
At something quiet and sensible, like *broderie anglaise*."

The King prowled the palace's tessellated floors;
He eavesdropped conversations, listened at open doors.
What he heard displeased him: his courtiers, one and all,
Were gushing with the gossip of the Butterfly Ball.

His Majesty was miffed. In a sudden fit of pique
He made a slow safari to far-off Mozambique
By way of Kilimanjaro, leaving his royal spoor
Between the sunlit snowcaps where the Eagle used to soar.

Not a bird made wing through the equatorial sky,
But the King did not pause to stop and wonder why;
And several nights elapsed, devoid of Nightingale song,
Before it slowly dawned on him that something was wrong.

Past Lake Tanganyika, where the water-wallowers steam
And the ripe, trampled pineapples so succulently gleam,
He glowered over Zambia, glared at the broad Zambesi;
And still he saw no birds. He grew restless and uneasy.

At length, in a clearing, Leonis chanced to see
A Hummingbird no bigger than a little Bumble-bee;
Sipping from hibiscus, it dipped a delicate bill
Deep for delicious nectar, hovering bright and still.

"Lovely jewel of our crown," King Lion said, "please say:
Where are your great cousins, our noble birds of prey?
Where are our Goldfinch, our Gannet and our Swan?
Where have all the members of our feathered family gone?"

"Sire," replied the Hummingbird, "I cannot tell a lie;
Every bird with big wings, of humble birth and high,
Has fled six thousand miles, to your kingdom's farthest part,
For the Party of Sir Perceval de Proude Peacock, Bart."

Then almighty anger rent the cloudless heaven asunder
With deep-throated rancour as reverberative as thunder;
The scruffneck Hyaena stifled his cackling laugh
And voiceless ever after was the stilt-legged Giraffe.

"That *nouveau riche* colonial! That foppish popinjay!
How *dare* he have pretensions to be so *distingué*,
Diminishing our glory with base grandiloquence,"
Roared Leonis the Mighty, with rabid eloquence.

His growl filled the world; and then it came to pass
That Leonis leapt home through the swishing elephant-grass.
All his subjects trembled: would his tantrum abate
Before he reached his palace with its massive bronze gate?

Shall the proud Sir Percy
Receive the royal mercy?
Does the King have it in mind
To be vengeful or kind?
Those close to him believe
He has something up his sleeve.

LORD OF THE JUNGLE

WHATEVER can vex
Leonis, Lord of the Golden Savanna,
Omnipotent Rex?
On his sovereign throne
King Lion alone
Commands enormous Africa's hosanna
From Morocco to the Cape, from Sudan to Sierra Leone.

With fury and fire
He has denounced the Peacock's disloyalty;
In regal attire,
And wearing the Ring
Of Authority, the King
Has averred, *No fowl may emulate Royalty:*
Sir Perceval's flaunting party was a trivial, vulgar fling.

A fanfare heralds His Majesty's decree:
What will the Peacock's punishment be?

More taut than a drum,
With every flinching ear cocked to listen,
The bush is struck dumb.
All the birds of the veld
And the jungle have knelt;
Lustrous as diadems and sceptres they glisten,
Begging the King's forgiveness, praying his anger may melt.

We hereby prescribe
(He smiles) *that we shall grant our lenience*
To the feathered tribe.
And we further ordain
That our Lord Chamberlain
Shall arrange a soirée *of such magnificence*
As shall never be known in the kingdom again!

The King has commanded a splendid cavalcade;
By whom shall all the arrangements be made?

CALCULUS, LORD CHAMBERLAIN

I 'M CALCULUS the Crocodile, do not misunderstand the smile
With which I favour all you *hoi polloi*;
I have a double denture which I'll use if peradventure
You should do the slightest thing that might annoy.

King Lion has commissioned me, expert in dactylonomy
    (Which means that I can count upon my digits),
To be his Tax Inspector, University Praelector,
    And Minister of Monuments and Midgets.

Master of the Ceremonies, Curator of the Cemeteries,
    I have a million grave considerations;
I'm Guardian of the Folio of Intrigue and Imbroglio,
    Transcender of the Royal Meditations.

I'm official Body-snatcher, I'm His Majesty's Back-scratcher,
    The Venerable Keeper of The Tusk;
Another high appointment is Custodian of The Ointment;
    I'm Chancellor of Darkness after dusk.

Now since the Peacock Party, the King (once hale and hearty)
    Has slid into a slow and sad decline;
By his recent Grand Decree we're to have a Jamboree
    And the huge responsibility is mine.

It is my solemn duty to prepare a night of beauty
    To exhilarate, bedazzle and entrance;
We shall have a masquerade and a carnival parade
    With all that's best of magic, song and dance.

Fantastical and comic, our farrago of a frolic
    Will banish all the demons of the dark;
My most supreme attainment is as Lord of Entertainment,
    The Knight of Glee and Grand Symposiarch!

With magical powers beyond mortal ken,
The King's necromancer, Cassandra, knows when
The royal fun
May be begun.

CASSANDRA

*D*IBBERTY, Dabberty, Dubberty, Dan,
Am I a goat, or am I a man?
Dibberty, Dabberty, Dubberty, Dee,
What is the future that I can foresee?

My heart is wicked and my soul is black;
I conjure the signs of the Zodiac.

My bones are yellow and my blood is gall;
Images form in my crystal ball.

The serpent fang of my finger nail
Spits out stars like a storm of hail.

Capricorn, Scorpio, Dragon and Bear;
I gather the Universe out of the air.

When shall be a propitious day?
Only the planets I summon shall say.

How they align when Leonis grins
Shall decide when the great festivity begins!

What kind of maker of magic am I?
Dibberty, Dabberty, Dubberty, DIE.
The horns of the Devil sprout out of my head,
Dibberty, Dabberty, Dubberty, DEAD.

The show is under way! The curtain rises soon
On a ballerina lighter than a hot-air balloon.

THE BALLERINA

FROM torrid Siam to the snows of Alaska
    The best impresarios bandy my name;
I'm Madame Pavlovna Modesté Nijinska,
    The Dowager Countess of *Nutcracker* fame.

Although I'm the object of much adulation,
    The darling of emperors, nabobs and tsars,
Between each and every standing ovation
    I'm more highly strung than a thousand guitars.

They loved my depiction of tragic Narcisse,
    Adored me in *Sylphides, Swan Lake* and *Giselle*;
In the Romanoff Theatre's tattling coulisse
    It's whispered that Benois once loved me as well.

       (Fouetté et jeté,
       Ma belle pirouette,
       Je fais la gargouillade en l'air;
       Assemblés et coupés,
       Ma svelte silhouette,
       Enfin je descendrai à terre.)

Tonight I'm commanded by Leonine Majesty!
    Have I my customary panache and flair?
My tummy has butterflies! Oh, what a travesty
    If I should fall down on my trim *derrière*!

We have a new ballet, *The Sea-birth of Venus*,
    That's choreographed by one William Shrimpe;
His steps are demanding: pray God I'm not seen as
    His first *assoluta* to land with a limp.

The curtain is rising! All weightless I waft,
    A gossamer feathering midsummer shores;
The lightest breath lifts me, I'm carried aloft
    Till I drown in the surf of tumultuous applause.

We humans cling to strands of hope
When full of worry and despair:
If only we could climb its rope
To untold happiness somewhere!

THE FAKIR

MYSTERIOUS as a cloud assembling through
A summer sky's intensity of blue,
A sudden figuration from thin air
Disturbingly but beautifully there,
From some far-off and half-forgotten age
An instant Fakir fills our empty stage.

His home is farther than the farthest star,
In Days-Gone-By, where all things wondrous are
Preserved for ever from the clutch of time:
For in that land where clocks can never chime
Or tick the precious hours of life away
It takes eternity to make one day.

He now performs the rope-trick. At his word
A silken hank uncoils and, like a bird
That trails a plaited tail, it starts to fly
Upright, as though suspended from the sky.
Then, one by one, without a trace of fear,
The animals all climb and disappear.

The last one gone, the Magic Fakir makes
A writhing forest grow of scaly snakes;
And, all amid the weird serpent-dance,
He rises slowly, cast into a trance.
He floats in space ten feet above the floor...
A puff of smoke — and he is seen no more!

In the best of all worlds, no home would be without
An oriental tea-pot with a magical spout.

WU CHENG-EN

AND NEXT — the Inscrutable Wizard of Kiangsu!
(There is no magic that he can't do,
From sleight of hand to feats of levitation,
Hocus-pocus to prestidigitation.)

Tonight he performs with the Dragon-Cornucopia
Presented to him by the Emperor of Utopia;
With an *Abracadabra, hey presto,* see
The tea-party poured by the witching Chimpanzee!

All alive-o, in a madcap jumble,
　　Crockery, dainties and silverware tumble,
Slices of flan, a gingerbread man,
　　Battenburg lavished with rich marzipan,
Coconut whispers and cherry-top cakes
　　Better than any *pâtissier* bakes,
Cream horns and custards and crumbly meringue,
　　Linked chipolatas of savoury tang,
Pastries and pies and a Swiss jam roll,
　　Jellies and trifles and profiteroles,
Biscuits and teaspoons and endless festoons
　　Of sugar mice, gâteaux and sweet macaroons:
Will you have apple strudel or a chocolate éclair?
　　There's more than enough for us all to share!

(And before he returns to his Chinese pagoda
The Mystery Man adds a brilliant coda
Of cool lemonade
In a sparkling cascade
And a bowl overflowing with ice cream soda!)

Proving that the whole
Is more than the sum of the parts
Must surely be the goal
Of the theatrical arts.

THE GORILLA CIRCUS

WHO IS this impresario
Grinning with glee and guile?
It's Captain Ali Gator,
Who's voyaged many a mile
With his circus since embezzling
The funds of The Bank of the Nile.

Circumnavigating Earth
Via Mexico and Manila,
The Captain's mad menagerie
Embarks in a small flotilla
Of tugs that tow the hulk of
Gargantisa the Gorilla.

Now, as any ancient mariner
Well knows, it's commonplace
On ocean-going vessels
To be so short of space
That often, on the quarter-deck,
They have to splice a brace.

So, all of Gator's animals
Have taken the form of two:
Wander the world for ever,
But I would wager you
Will never find a more bizarre
Amphibological zoo.

Sea-lion, Dog-fish, Tiger-Moth!
What monstrous handicraft
Has gone into the making
Of a creature quite as daft
As Turtle-Dove, soft feathers fore
And armour-plating aft?

Captain Gator's fear of shipwreck
Accounts for his haunted stare:
When Sea-Horse was washed overboard
He acquired a new Night-Mare
Which whinnies about ruin
And a cupboard perpetually Bear.

The pachyderm Rhinoceros creates quite a stir,
Parading all the terrors of the Earth that ever were.

THE EPIC PROCESSION

AND NOW began the cavalcade:
Floats, in a slow procession
Of Herculean grandeur, made
A dignified progression,
Portraying every epic theme that's known
On tumbrils rumbling past the royal throne.

The WEATHERS OF THE WORLD rolled by
With Earthquake, Tempest, Ice and Flood
Beneath a dome of endless Sky
Where Sunrise rinsed the Clouds in blood
And molten lava, flung from loud Volcanoes,
Solidified in Arctic Hurricanoes.

Behind them, ELECTRICITY
Picked up fallen Thunderbolts
And crackling with alacrity
Turned them into Amps and Volts;
A dynamo of verve, he made his mark —
Potentially, the evening's brightest spark.

Then all the ELEMENTS came in:
Ethereal Miss Helium,
Base old Iron, Sir Cornish Tin,
Unstable Lord Uranium,
And Vesta Phosphorus who, with acrimony,
Rubbed shoulders with abrasive Antimony.

All huge events of HISTORY
Went past, as though they'd never cease:
Creation's every mystery
Of Love and Beauty, Harmony, Peace —
Till Demons of Black Havoc and Satan's Law
Dragged Rhino in as Mars, the God of WAR.

Lo! She approaches, most wondrous to behold,
The purring lady with a heart of pure gold.

THE JAGUAR LADY

NO SUN ever shone upon lost El Dorado.
Queen Serenissima, Sovereign of Night,
Empress of Lambency, Princess of Lustre,
Prohibits her empire to heavenly light:

For the glow of a solitary, mist-milky star
Would multiply fifty quintillionfold
If mirrored among all her gilt cordilleras
And nugget-hewn cities of luculent gold,

Bedazzling soft Sloth in the Kruger-rand palm,
Goldfinch and Goldcrest and forest-floor folk —
The pliant Armadillo, the odd Pangolin
With scales like the leaves of a globe artichoke.

So only her eyes may illumine the dusk
Of a continent far beyond man-charted land,
Where ingots bestrew every limitless seashore,
Embedded in gold-dust as common as sand.

Imagine that country of marigold landscape
That gleams in the darkness when she is awake
And the beam of her gaze brings a glistering autumn
To the gold-leaf thickets by the bullion lake!

> *Aztec-diademed, the Jaguar lady*
> *Appears before King Lion and unlocks*
> *Caskets of gifts for His Golden Majesty:*
> *Vases, trinkets and a musical box*
> *Of monkeys made from melted doubloons*
> *Playing selections of golden old tunes.*

Beware, after nightfall, if the jungle's tinder-dry,
Lest the terrifying sparks of the Tiger start to fly.

THE TIGER

THEN fell a darkness, as of a diamond mine
  Deep underground
 Where gems of a blinding brilliance lie,
  Yet to be found;
And into the mineral silence, menacing,
  There came the sound

Of something new-born and of terrible power
  Engendered by fire
In the cellars of Chaos by flame-fingered demons
  White-hot as desire
Tending the flambeaux and smouldering braziers
  Of Vulcan's empire.

The fizz of its insistent whispering hissed
  In the jungle night
As a fuse of saltpetre lit at Earth's centre
  Raced up to ignite
The Pyrotechnic Tiger from Royal Bengal
  Who burned as bright

As a billion diamonds brought into the sunshine,
  A tapestry
Of filaments incandescent with fire-birds
  And the poetry
Of Salamanders, Dragons and Phoenixes ablaze
  In perfect symmetry.

What better, to beguile the final hours
Of darkness, than some special fruits and flowers?

FLORA ZOOLOGICA

CHAMELEON, the Colour-Master, now
Regales his royal audience with a bow,
Announcing that a brilliant bouquet
Will close the cavalcade with a display
Of creatures who, this night of nights, he claims,
Will demonstrate the aptness of their names.

Transmogrified, the Tiger Lily prowls
Through thickets where the watchful Dog Rose growls
At Puss Moth poised to spring on dainty paws
From ripe Crab Apples armed with pincering claws.

Gaggles of Goose Berries glide upon the cool
Undimpled waters of a summer pool
Where Crocodilia sinisterly lurk
For Turtle Flowers paddling through the murk.

The monocled Sir Dandy Lion twirls
His curled moustachios and ogles girls
Like Lady Bird, whose feathers lift her higher
Than Dragon Flies can hover, breathing fire.

While Monkey Flowers chatter, hunting for fleas,
And Horse Chestnuts gallop under the trees,
Chameleon elaborates his joke
With a Toad Lily that can hop and croak.

Can you spot others of this curious ilk,
Like Spider Orchid spinning her fine silk?
Next time the Sun Flower beams by dazzling night
With three waxing Moon Flowers just as bright,
You'll surely hear, high in the southern sky,
Herds of Elephant Moth stampeding by.

Performers who wish to conserve their sang-froid
Should conserve rather less of their avoirdupois.

THE COMPANY OF PORKE

WHEN it was noticed that nothing had made
His Majesty smile through the whole cavalcade,
A courtier whispered, "It is my belief
Our pageant could do with some comic relief."

His neighbour, consulting his programme, opined
That everyone present was of a like mind;
But could they expect *A Midsummer Night's Dream*
To provide what was needed: a right-royal scream?

The curtains were parted and — how *infra dig*!
The King of the Fairies was played by a Pig:
None other than Herbert de Mandible Tusker,
That ever-so-awful Shakespearean busker;

And no one had witnessed a spectacle zanier
Than Gammonie Rasha, his wife, as Titania.
"If *Bacon* had written the Works of the Bard,"
The courtier tittered, "those mountains of lard

"Might be more appropriate. Oh, what a sham!
How they both *hog* the stage, how they both *ham*!
That bore of a boar, how ungainly he totters;
And see how she *minces* on delicate trotters!"

King Lion embarrassedly bit on his knuckle,
Unable to stifle a runaway chuckle;
And all of a sudden his happy and glorious
Shoulders were shaking with laughter uproarious.

He cackled and guffawed, he sniggered and giggled, he
Roared when the actors fell higgledy-piggledy,
Tickled that humbug and jiggery-pokery
Ended with farcical piggery-jokery.

The Fireflies in the footlights are extinguished
        One by one;
The marvellous spectacular is finished,
        Over and done.

The theatre is empty. Janitor Reynard
        Brings his brush;
And while he sweeps, the Royals ride homeward,
        And the dawn thrush

Keeps chirruping this message: "There's no reason
        And no rhyme
Why jollity shouldn't be thought in season
        Any old time."